# A Wish for a Fish

Written by
Jill Atkins

Illustrated by
Heike Jane Zimmermann

Ransom

Josh and his dog Pong had a shell.

"This is a wishing shell, Pong.
I shall wish for a fish on a dish."

3

Josh and Pong ran to the shed.

They got a fishing rod.

We need a hook, Pong.

Woof!

They ran to the fishing shop.

They got a sharp hook.

Now we can go fishing.
I will sing songs to the fish.
I will get a fish on my
hook.

They sat in a ship.

Josh hung the bait on the hook.
He sang songs to the fish.

Whoosh! The rod was in the air.

Then Josh had a shock.

He had a fish on his hook.

The fish was big, with long fangs.

Josh got the fish on the ship.

9

The fish shot off the ship and fell back in.

Pong was sad.

They ran to the fish shop.

They got fish and chips for supper!